TRINITY
COLLEGE LONDON

G000163155

Octave — Somewhere (
Major 7th — Incomplete
Minor 7th — somewhere (u
Major 6th — Dashing through the snow
Minor 6th — creepy version of above
perfect 5th — Chasing cars
Perfect 4th — Away in a manger
Major 3rd — start of adele
Minor 3rd — Greensleeves
Major 2nd — scale
Minor 2nd — Jaws.

Unison

Guitar Grade 4
Pieces & Exercises
for Trinity College London examinations

2010-2015

Published by:
Trinity College London
89 Albert Embankment
London SE1 7TP UK

T +44 (0)20 7820 6100
F +44 (0)20 7820 6161
E music@trinitycollege.co.uk
www.trinitycollege.co.uk

Music processed by Artemis Music Ltd.
Printed in England by Halstan, Amersham, Bucks.

Pavana

Arcangelo dal Liuto
(16th century)

3

Bourrée

from Cello Suite no. 3 BWV 1009

Johann Sebastian Bach
(1685-1750)

Pavana + Bourrée

Bagatella

op. 73 no. 3

Mauro Giuliani
(1781–1829)

5

Pastorale

op. 21 no. 16

Matteo Carcassi
(1792–1853)

Ejercicio

no. 2 from *Colección 12a de Ejercicios*

José Ferrer
(1835-1916)

Nostalgia

Cees Hartog
(born 1949)

Steely Blue

Vincent Lindsey-Clark
(born 1956)

Garden Steps

Andrew York
(born 1958)

(*1*) Let A on string ③ ring throughout these three bars.

Buen augurio

Máximo Diego Pujol
(born 1957)

Technical Suite (Exercises)

Candidates choosing Option ii) Technical Suite in the Technical Work section of the examination must prepare the following exercises.

1. Arabesque (slurs)

To be prepared *apoyando* or *tirando* at candidate's choice.*

2. Clair de Lune (half barré and arpeggios)

To be prepared *tirando*.

(*1*) hinge barré

* *apoyando* = rest stroke; *tirando* = free stroke.

3. España (scales)

To be prepared *tirando*.

Energetically ♩ = 112–120

4. Skyline Melody (full barré)

♩ = 92–100

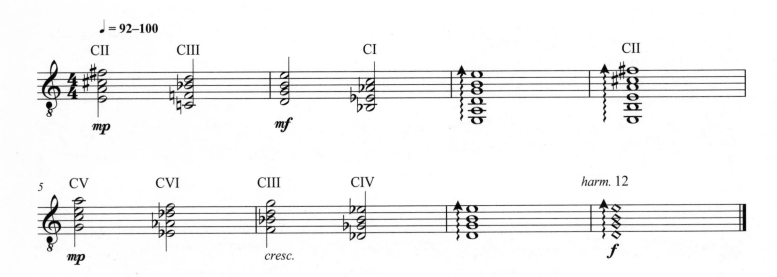